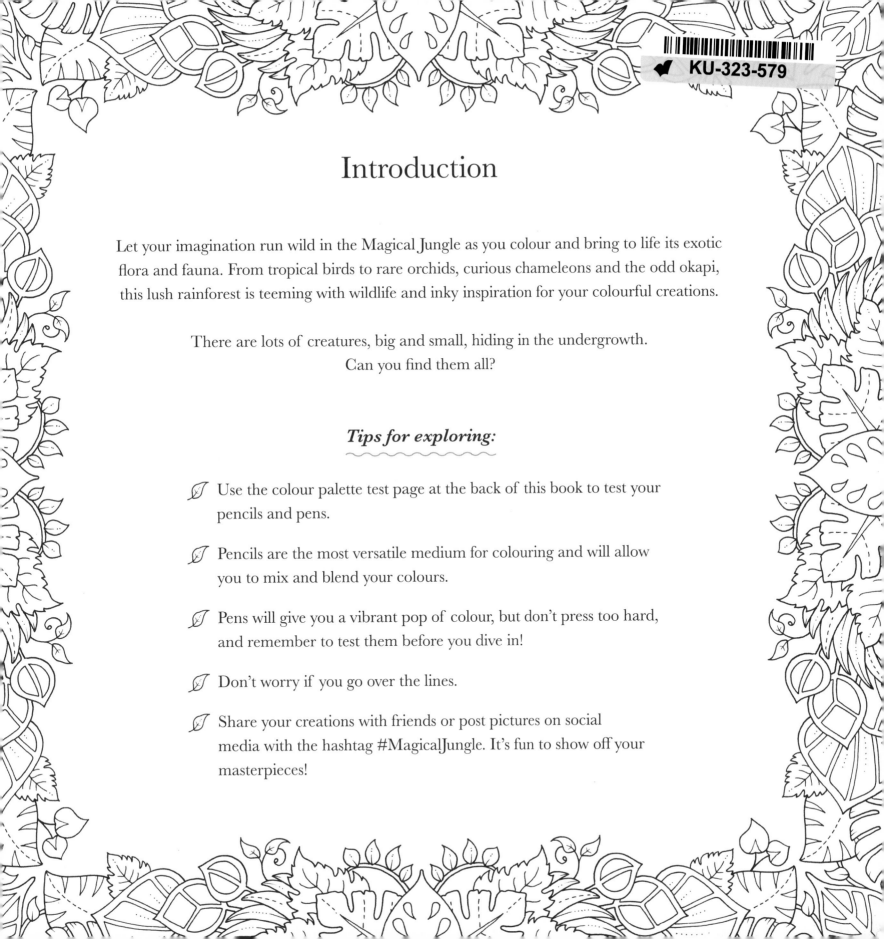

Introduction

Let your imagination run wild in the Magical Jungle as you colour and bring to life its exotic flora and fauna. From tropical birds to rare orchids, curious chameleons and the odd okapi, this lush rainforest is teeming with wildlife and inky inspiration for your colourful creations.

There are lots of creatures, big and small, hiding in the undergrowth.
Can you find them all?

Tips for exploring:

- Use the colour palette test page at the back of this book to test your pencils and pens.

- Pencils are the most versatile medium for colouring and will allow you to mix and blend your colours.

- Pens will give you a vibrant pop of colour, but don't press too hard, and remember to test them before you dive in!

- Don't worry if you go over the lines.

- Share your creations with friends or post pictures on social media with the hashtag #MagicalJungle. It's fun to show off your masterpieces!

Johanna Basford

Magical Jungle

An Inky Expedition & Colouring Book

2 4 6 8 10 9 7 5 3

Virgin Books, an imprint of Ebury Publishing,
20 Vauxhall Bridge Road,
London SW1V 2SA

Virgin Books is part of the Penguin Random House group of
companies whose addresses can be found at global.penguinrandomhouse.com

Penguin
Random House
UK

First published by Virgin Books in 2016
www.penguin.co.uk

A CIP catalogue record for this book is available from the British Library

ISBN 9780753557167

Penguin Random House is committed to a sustainable future for our
business, our readers and our planet. This book is made from
Forest Stewardship Council® certified paper.

MIX
Paper from
responsible sources
FSC® C018179
FSC
www.fsc.org

Interior designed by Johanna Basford and Sabrina Bowers
Printed and bound in Italy by L.E.G.O. S.p.A.

Hidden inside this book are ...

1 crocodile

4 hummingbirds

2 tigers

1 sloth

4 snakes

16 elephants

63 butterflies

7 lizards

4 chameleons

2 ants

1 spider

6 tropical birds

1 turtle

5 snails

1 stork

1 panda

13 dragonflies

13 beetles

20 parrots

9 monkeys

1 okapi

5 toucans

1 jungle nymph

1 hippo

3 lemurs

7 frogs

17 fish

This book belongs to

....

Key to the Magical Jungle ...

1 crocodile, 1 elephant, 1 monkey, 1 parrot, 1 snake

1 monkey, 1 parrot   1 butterfly, 1 dragonfly,
                       1 parrot

2 butterflies, 2 tropical birds   2 hummingbirds

3 butterflies, 2 parrots, 1 monkey

1 butterfly   1 butterfly

2 butterflies, 1 chameleon, 1 frog, 1 okapi

2 butterflies, 1 snail, 1 tiger   1 butterfly, 1 toucan

2 beetles, 2 hummingbirds   2 frogs, 2 toucans

7 butterflies, 2 dragonflies, 1 parrot

1 butterfly   1 beetle, 1 butterfly

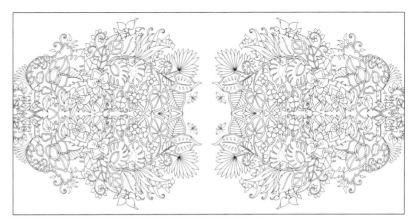

4 dragonflies

2 dragonflies, 1 panda

1 lizard

15 butterflies

1 ant, 1 chameleon

1 ant, 1 lizard

7 butterflies

2 lemurs, 1 snake

3 monkeys, 1 lizard

2 monkeys, 1 sloth, 1 toucan, 1 tropical bird

8 beetles

4 butterflies

1 spider

1 butterfly, 1 jungle nymph

1 snail

1 butterfly, 1 frog, 1 monkey, 1 snake

5 fish, 1 hippo

1 snail, 1 stork

1 frog

10 fish, 1 snail, 1 turtle

2 fish, 1 frog   3 dragonflies, 1 lizard

2 chameleons, 1 butterfly   14 elephants, 10 parrots

2 lizards

3 butterflies   1 beetle, 1 elephant

3 tropical birds

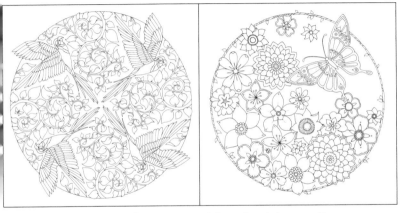

4 parrots, 1 butterfly · · · · · 1 beetle, 1 butterfly

4 butterflies

1 butterfly, 1 frog, 1 lizard, 1 toucan

1 dragonfly · · · · · 1 tiger

2 butterflies, 1 lemur, 1 snail, 1 snake

Colour Palette Test Page

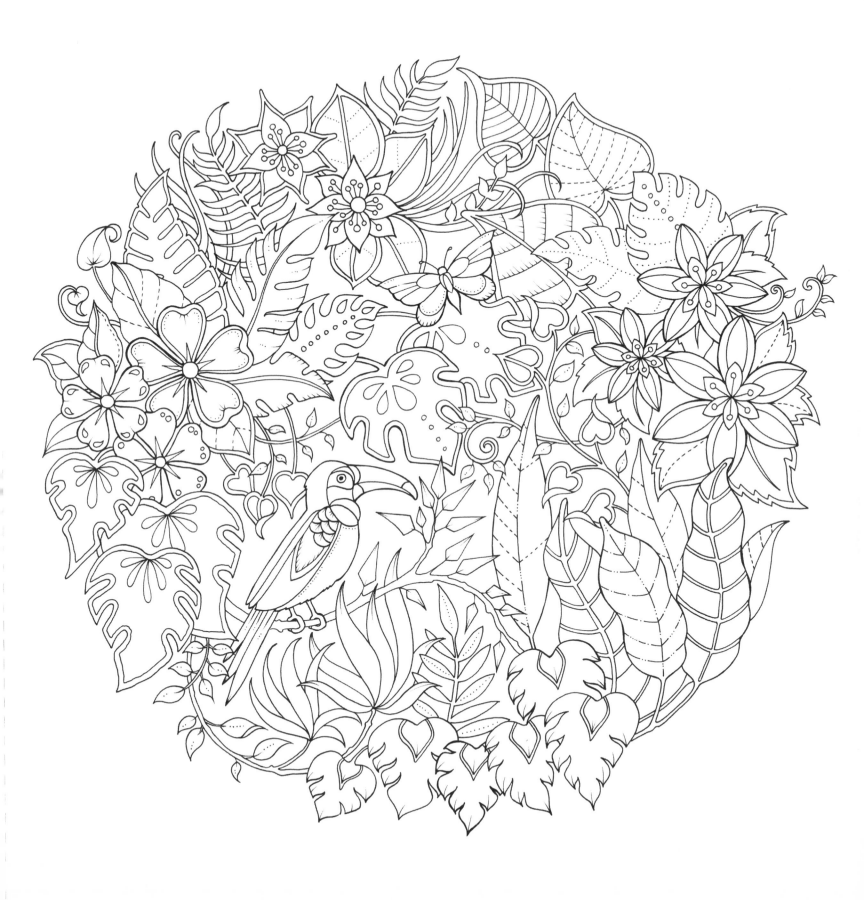